ILLUST

ORAL
SEX

THE
ILLUSTRATED BOOK
OF
ORAL
SEX

by

Annie Blinkhorn

London
THE *Erotic* Print Society

First Published February 2002
Reprinted September 2002

ACKNOWLEDGEMENTS

Annie Blinkhorn would like to thank:

Jamie Maclean, Tim Hobart, Michael Kammerling, Chris Peachment, Chris Hart, Jonathan Green, Dr David Delvin, Oliver Maitland. Thanks to Rowan for nagging me to write in the first place.
A debt of gratitude to my enthusiastic and ever-eager research assistant who knew no limits in the search for oral perfection. Special thanks and love to Nick for the laptop and encouragement.

For their help with this edition the Publishers would like to thank:

John and Linda DuPret
Eric Wilkins

Frontispeice: **Cheripoulos, French (fl. 1920-1940)**
Illustration to *La Roman de Violette*
J'arrive!
Preceding page: **Louis André Berthommé-Saint-André, French (1905–1977)**
Illustration from Paul Verlaine's *Œuvres Libres.*
"Sit, Girl, just *sit!*"
Opposite: **Anon, French (circa 1930)**
Lesbian Lovers **(The DuPret Collection)**

OPEN WIDE

Whilst reminiscing about great holidays and happy childhood memories, my friend Rachael noticed that all her fondest recollections were in one way or another connected with food. The happiest she had been in her life was whilst masticating, the primary source of pleasure for her being between the lips. Therapists, sexperts and my colleagues at *The Erotic Review* are fond of trotting out the old, "the brain is the largest and most important sex organ" line, but there are some, myself and Rachael amongst them, that are more inclined to believe it's the gob. The mouth is certainly my most erogenous zone. It just happens to be the one on my boyfriend's face.

Second only to getting a smacked arse, the first human experience is of contact through the mouth, nourished at the mother's breast. Once off the tit, the baby immediately sucks its thumb as a comforting nipple-replacement. My publisher has two small children and assures me that an early stage of infant development is sticking anything and everything into its mouth; food, fingers, sticklebricks, soil, worms; deciphering as to whether something is nice or nasty depending on what it feels and tastes like in there.

With adulthood and sexual awakening the desire to wrap your gnashers round something satisfying has not diminished. Time and again those lists of what men and women find

---

Louis André Berthommé-Saint-André, French (1905–1977)
Illustration to Pierre Louÿs' *Pibrac*
Now *that's* what we call room service.

Above: **Léon Courbouleix**, French (fl. 1930s)
Suzon en Vacances
"Why Miss Frobisher, I see you've already
become acquainted with the rest of my staff!"
Following pages: **Paul Avril**, French (1849-1928)
From *De Figuris Veneris*
"So this is what they mean by the Lays of Ancient Rome?"

attractive in the other, the mouth, or at least 'smile' will be high up in the sex appeal charts. A gorgeous smacker is incredibly alluring, particularly a wide and beautiful mouth on a woman. Without getting too Desmond Morris here, one can see why a glossy pair of pouting lips can be read as an indication of a sexually swollen glistening twin pair down below. John Cleland's woman of pleasure, Fanny Hill, describes her vulva as "the pouting-lipt mouth". Look at pictures of contemporary pin-ups – Kylie Minogue, Angelina Jolie, Liz Hurley, Jordan, Pamela Anderson, and you will find that their expressions in most publicity shots are pure wouldn't-my-lips-look-good-round-your-dick pout-fests. It can't be a coincidence that the latter three women have collagen-enhanced mouths. Jordan has posed for cover shots for men's mag *GQ* with a line of Swarovski crystal stick-on, er, *tadpoles* swimming towards her mouth.

And the last in the list we *know* is a cocksucker, her oral-manipulation skills as

demonstrated on her former husband Tommy 'T-bone' Lee immortalised on home video which was subsequently stolen and broadcast globally.

Marilyn Monroe's complex make-up regime was reputed to involve an intricate lipstick application which embodied her sex-appeal formula – one of simultaneous innocence and voluptousness. Her lips were painted to look like, "a guy could just slide his cock between them". The visual and sensory focus of Salvador Dali's Mae West room is a sofa in the shape of the great dame's red, puckered pout. The piece of furniture draws the viewer's eye, as if one would be sucked in and swallowed alive were one to perch upon it.

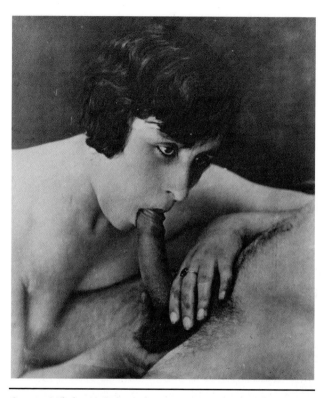

Opposite: Mihaly von Zichy, Hungarian (1827-1906)
Illustration from *Liebe*
"And this is only the *beginning!*"
Above: Anon, French (circa 1930)
The Young Fellatrice (The DuPret Collection)
Lost in a fellatory reverie.

The effect is not cannibal but overwhelmingly sexual. My immensely helpful research assistant raided the library for literary references to oral sex. He cast aside Nabokov's *Lolita* as not having relevant content, but the book's cover shows one of the most famous erotically charged images of the silver screen, albeit illicit. If there were ever a cinema 'still' that poignantly captured the exquisite and painful sexual allure of a female mouth it is that of Sue Lyons, the fifteen year old actress peeping out over heart-shaped sunglasses with a bright red lollipop sticking half in and half out a scarlet-painted mouth. The whole moral issue of the book is encapsulated in that photo – does she know what she is doing with that lollipop?

On the subject of young women, lollipops and dirty old fuckers, that notorious lover and crooner Serge Gainsbourg wrote a tune, *Les Sucettes*, to be sung by the teenage France Gall the words of which concerned the delights of sucking on a lollipop. The whole dirty ditty was an

---

Feodor Rojankovski, Latvian (fl. 1920-1950)
Illustration from *Vers Libres*
"Oh I do love a nice outdoor prick-nic."

Above: Feodor Rojankovski, Latvian (fl. 1920-1950)
Illustration from *Paris Spring, 1933*
Hors d'oeuvre (or is this the *entrée*?)
Opposite: Anon, French (circa 1930)
Honeymoon Couple I (The DuPret Collection)
"Darling, I *think* we've got damp."
"Well, I *know* I have, Dearest."

incredibly obvious and explicit reference to fellatio and was absolutely scandalous,

(sample lyrics: *Annie loves lollipops/ scented with aniseed/ the syrup pours down her throat/ she's in Paradise/ all she has left on her tongue is the little stick*)

Mlle. Gall claimed to have no idea about its not-so-hidden meaning. On its discovery she never worked for or spoke to Gainsbourg again. I mean, for goodness sake, what did she expect getting involved with the grubby Gallic git anyway?

The power of a pair of fellatio-worthy lips is not lost on those canny boys in the advertising biz. I used to think the comparison between chocolate bars and phallic symbolism a load of over-analytical crap. But then I considered the wide-eyed maidens in overflowing baths and poppy-strewn cornfields slipping the crumbliest,

---

Eric Wilkins, British (contemporary)
Fellatio
"Mmm… *saucisson sec* for breakfast - my *favourite*!"

Above: Jean Dulac, French (active 1920-1940)
Illustration from *Nous Deux*
"And the curtains are Osborne & Little, I think…"
Opposite: Feodor Rojankovski, Latvian (fl. 1920-1950)
Illustration from Pierre Louÿs' *Poésies Erotiques*

flakiest milk chocolate in the world into a wet-look pout from that very successful, famous and long-running commercial. Cadbury's Flakes are a bugger to eat, the damn thing gets everywhere, but show a buxom bird giving the choccy a blow-job with her eyes shut in delirious satisfaction and you have a sophisticated and sexy bit of confectionary. Tube stations and bus stops all over the country carry an ad depicting a dusky babe staring out of the picture, nibbling on a gargantuan ice cream bar, tantalisingly cracking the hard chocolate coating. The fact that she's pushing a lolly with the powerful, masculine

name of 'Magnum' into her mush says to me that she is not so much eating a pleasant dairy-based sweet, but going down on it (or maybe I took GCSE media studies too seriously). And if a terrific, spine-tingling kiss isn't the very definition of good oral sex, I don't know what is.

Anon, French (circa 1930)
Oral Trio I (The DuPret Collection)
"Now Boys, don't get *too* friendly, it's *me* you should be concentrating on!"

GETTING DOWN TO IT

But enough of coy talk of kisses and candy-bars, time to put my money where my mouth is. Why is oral sex so good? In my opinion the practice of playing the pink oboe or drinking from the furry cup is not merely foreplay or a pale

Preceding page: Gaston Barret, French (fl. 1950s)
Illustration to *Lettres à la Marquise, l'Adam lascif*
"In all my days as Secretary to the Downshire Ramblers,
I've never seen such a fine specimen of *Phallus Impudicus*, Mr Smith!"
Above: Eric Wilkins, British (contemporary)
The Eager Apprentice
"Excuse me, Hilary, I think it's *my* turn now."

imitation of sexual intercourse, it is the apotheosis of lovemaking. Of all the routes to orgasm, getting head is the ultimate in pure carnal indulgence. When the time comes to finding out about the birds and the bees, we are taught that genitals are really supposed to go around or inside other genitals, that's their function. Which makes them, in terms of propagation, a design triumph. So climax brought about by something other than straight sex, i.e. buggery, masturbation and oral sex has nothing to do with babies and therefore somehow unnecessary, licentious, unnatural, *vice*. Oh good. Po-faced disapproval of the wonderful activity only serves to spur on the enthusiasm for the true sexual libertine. Oral is both a gratifying sex act and an effective form of contraceptive but the onanistic and therefore hedonistic qualities of a tonguing performed on the male are horrifying to some quarters. Notably the church, which regards the spilling of seed either on the ground or in any moist and willing orifice other than the vagina to be strictly *verboten*. Amongst the list of cardinal sins of the Catholic church is *seminem in ore*, literally, 'semen in the mouth'.

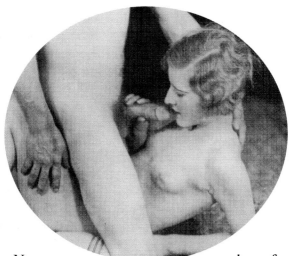

Not so much for men as for the female who gives lip-action, there seems to be a stigma attached to the fact that the practitioner is active/willing/enthusiastic. Trying to unearth pre-20th century accounts of fellatio in fiction was less fruitful than I originally imagined. Even De Sade doesn't appear to go an enormous bundle on it, preferring to concentrate on torture and excrement. This is possibly because intercourse in fiction has always been ever so slightly forced upon the heroine or is otherwise offered by a woman of loose morals. Oral intercourse however is, in most cases, a difficult thing to physically force upon a woman and requires her cooperation, if not instigation, which isn't an image befitting a herione, no matter how racy the novel. Equally men have perpetuated some mythology about the woman that goes down on them. In the film *Analyze This* Billy Crystal's shrink asks Robert de Niro's mobster what his wife can't give him that his mistress can. We know it's blow jobs when he says: "because that's the mouth she has to kiss my children with". It's a funny line but the point is that with his spouse, straight, reproductive sex is ok, but good girls don't take lunch downtown.

I'm afraid to say it but blow jobs have been given a bad rap, or a least the idea of a skilled fellatrice going at it with gusto, who believes that chocolate comes second only to semen in its yumminess, has. So too has the tight-lipped miss who recoils with horror at giving the old chap

---

Anon, French (circa 1920)
The First Time (The DuPret Collection)
Bernice was uncertain what to do next.

Above: Anon, French School, (circa 1930)
Illustration from *Confidences de Celestine*
That's enough, Jean, I'm late for the City as it is.
Opposite: Anon, French (circa 1930)
Oral Trio II (The DuPret Collection)
"Really you two, I'm beginning to despair!"

downstairs a little kiss. Like girls-who-do and girls-who-don't 'put out' in terms of sexual intercourse, eating the meat also has a schizophrenic image to say the least. Whilst there are fellatio workshops in America for professional women and upper-middle class housewives who are anxious lest their husbands should stray, there are countless gags, if you'll forgive the pun, about 'er indoors's reluctance to gobble knob; Q: Why is oral sex like lobster? A: You don't get either at home.

Above: Gaston Barret, French (fl. 1950s)
Illustration to *Lettres à la Marquise, l'Adam lascif*
"Umph, umph, mmumnn, gurg, mmm!"
Following page: Anon, French (circa 1930)
Busy Girls (The DuPret Collection)
"You have no idea how much I appreciate
you bringing your friend along, Diane."

I did hear, or perhaps I should say 'witnessed', several other terrific oral sex jokes with which I was regaled when I sought advice and anecdotes for this book; unfortunately, I cannot repeat them here, not out of a desire to remain within the bounds of good taste, but because they involved props, amongst them a glass of milk and a banana – I'm sure, dear reader, you could just as easily guess their comedic place in a joke about chowing down.

The way to a man's heart may be through his stomach, but the key to his soul, (his bank account, a clothing allowance and unlimited access to a penthouse suite) is captured through devotion to getting on yours knees with your mouth open. If he does not have any of the aforementioned attractions, then look upon it as a valuable device of distracting him from *Match of the Day* and then after a climax that leaves him drained like a post crew-cut Samson, tell him about the accident with the car. If there can be such a thing as an almost-universal truth then it is "all men love blow-jobs". I have, in the course of my research, met one or two who preferred to give than to receive oral (and we were very happy together, for a while...) but on the whole, they cannot get enough of it. After all, ladies, when

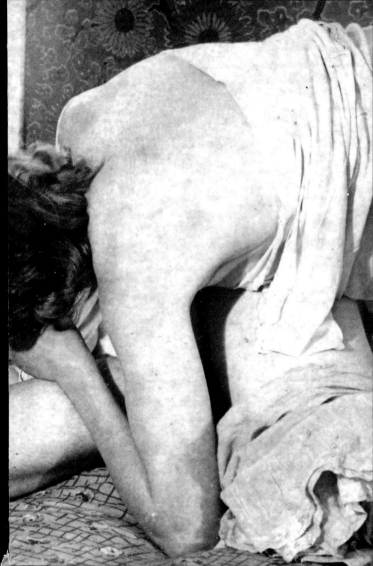

Above: Anon, French (circa 1930)
Scene in a Paris Brothel (The DuPret Collection)
"We should never have let Lawrence Llewellen-Bowen decorate this room. "
Opposite: Cheripoulos, French (fl. 1920-1940)
Illustration to *La Roman de Violette*

was the last time you heard him say, "Darling, do I have to come in your mouth *again*?". The negative image of being prepared to blow comes from the male suspicion, almost disbelief, that any girl would actually to put his prick between her lips with delight, as much as he might desperately desire it. As a very close male friend told me, "There you are; a wanking teenager, you hardly dare imagine you'll ever show your todger to a female never mind that a girl might volunteer to suck on it one day!" Another friend clearly finds the gift of the gob reassuring, "I mean say for instance you have a one night stand and she goes down on you, it's an unspoken commitment,

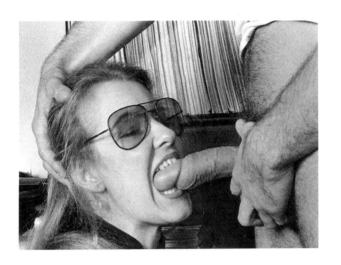

you think 'this girl *likes* me, she must do if she wants to suck my cock.'" A recurring opinion emerged during my enquiries; men love it, but assume they are getting a favour, and not that the lady friend in question would actually *choose* to do it.

Sadly, because knob-hobbing has these associations of submission and/or slack morals, fellatory insults have long been in the profane lexicon. 'Cocksucker' for instance is a term used to describe an irredeembaly horrid person and the definition of the US colloquial fuck-you sentiment, 'Bite it!' is "1980s US phr. of aggressive dismissal, 'it' is the penis [or posterior]" according to Jonathon

Green's indispensable *Dictionary of Slang* (Cassell). Mr Green has been kind enough to furnish me with over 150 synonyms on this subject from the visually imaginative 'knock the dust off the old sombrero' to the sweetly rhyming

*Opposite:*Eric Wilkins, British (contemporary)
Hunger I
Prunella Bites.
Above: Louis André Berthommé-Saint-André, French (1905–1977)
The New Hat
"It's customary to shake the vicar's *hand* after the service Edna."

'moofty-poofty'. Most euphemisms for the wonderful deed are, I'm afraid to say, schoolboy slang and verging on the vile – 'gobble the goop', 'mouth-fuck' and 'skull-buggery' to name a few, although I must admit that there's no mistaking their meaning, and they make more sense than *blow*job. Although it's a bit of a shame that some of the most obscene insults relate to this beautiful act, one of the most (unintentionally) funny scenes in cinema history is the possessed rasping voice emerging from Linda Blair in *The Exorcist*. Is "Your mother sucks cocks in Hell" the worst slander she could come up with? It's now so famous and almost camp, that it's as harmful as a playground taunt.

Eric Wilkins, British (contemporary)
Hunger II
"Words fail me, Penny"
"Mmmm…"

Above: Marcel Vertès, Hungarian (1895-1961)
Illustration from Pierre Louÿs' *Poésies Erotiques*
"Griselda's tongue-work left her consort feeling a little drawn."
Opposite: Mihaly von Zichy, Hungarian (1827-1906)
Illustration from *Liebe*
Deep Throat, circa 1860

CELEBRITY SUCKERS

O ral sex is hardly the exclusive ground of the kinkiest rubbered-up sex fiends, but some of the most famous sex scandals of recent history have been added extra flavour with the inclusion of this kind of intercourse. Christ, a little bit of head has been known to make some women (if only for a while), and break others. Bored, lonely and horny Hugh Grant picked up prostitute Divine Brown to get sucked off, nothing that thousands of hookers aren't doing all the time. Her arrest turned her world around. She became instantly famous.

Grant just refined his bumbling, floppy-haired, apologetic Englishman. But Brown, interviews which had formerly meant a routine hauling in with the LAPD, now were conducted by Richard and Judy in front of cameras *and* she got paid for them. Grant's

Preceding page: **Achille Déveria**, French (1800-1857)
Illustration from Alfred de Musset's *Gamiani*
Soixante-neuf never looked simpler than in the Romantic era.
Above: **Anon**, French (circa 1930)
Oral Trio III (The DuPret Collection)
"Well, *that's* more like it!"
Opposite: **Louis André Berthommé-Saint-André**, French (1905–1977)
La Suceuse

little mistake, to be explained away by him as a momentary lapse of judgement, was Brown's meal ticket. Sort of. Eager to be something in H o l l y w o o d (other than a call-girl) she made it into film. A couple of porn titles were released and gained press attention on the back of Divine Brown's appearance. Since then, nothing much: the world has forgotten Hugh's indiscretion and Ms Brown has dropped out of sight. As any career girl knows, you can only get so far on the one blow job, though she definitely milked that one dry.

Monica Lewinsky is another canny lass who capitalised on not keeping her big mouth shut. Best-selling biography, diets, cigars and various other forms of merchandising licensed in her

46

name made her rich whilst she demurely cast herself in the pose of naive, wide-eyed, wide-lipped intern. As with Hugh Grant, all is forgiven for Bill Clinton, happy in retirement playing golf and giving after dinner speeches. But for a considerable chunk of the late 90s, Bill's version

Opposite: **Anon, French (circa 1900)**
Soixante Neuf (The DuPret Collection)
Why the Victorians covered up piano legs.

Louis André Berthommé-Saint-André, French (1905–1977)
Above: ***What a Strange Taste!***
Overleaf: *The Mouthwash*

of reality, "I did not have sexual relations with that woman", threw up debate and discussion as to the moral nature of an extra-marital blow job. Although he did not have sex with Miss Lewinsky, if not Hillary, then many other wives and commentators in general did not perceive Clinton's activities to be presidentially uxorious.

Lewinsky and Brown came out of nowhere,

Above: **Albert Marquet, French (1875-1947)**
From *L'Académie des dames*
Opposite: **Eric Wilkins, British (contemporary)**
Hunger III
Rings on her fingers and cocks in her mouth.

chomped on a male member and became household names. For Margaret, Duchess of Argyll, her divorce and subsequent exile from high society was brought about chiefly by an incriminating Polaroid of her face attached to the penis of an unidentified man. Speculation of the headless figure has set off the rumour that the dick involved belonged to Douglas Fairbanks Jnr. To her remaining friends, the Duchess somewhat eccentrically maintained that the photo was a fake and that her head had been superimposed.

The most famous titbit involving celebrities

and cunnilingus is sadly pure myth. Immediately after the arrest of Mick Jagger and Keith Richards on drug charges came the anecdote that when the police raided the country house where The Rolling Stones were up to no good, the scene they

---

Opposite: Louis André Berthommé-Saint-André, French (1905–1977)
The Eager Little Shopgirl
Above: Anon, French (circa 1930)
Girl on Top (The DuPret Collection)
Heavenly twins, enormous in the imagination,
large in life, and all that lies between.

---

came upon was of Jagger eating a Mars Bar out of Marianne Faithfull's cunt. This became part of Stones rock mythology from that momenton. How fitting for a band with old rubberlips fronting them and a cartoon mouth with the tongue sticking out for a logo. There is a nod and a wink to the legend in the 1970 film *Performance* in which Jagger appears with another blonde, Keith Richard's girlfriend Anita Pallenberg (she and Jagger supposedly enjoyed actual penetration during the film's sex scenes). The milkman delivers not four pints of full cream

Opposite: Gaston Barret, French (fl. 1950s)
Illustration to *Lettres à la Marquise, l'Adam lascif*
"I think you'll find my cunt is another 45° darling."
Above: Eric Wilkins, British (contemporary)
Hunger IV
Thinks: 'Is this an orgasmic banana?'

but a box of Mars Bars. Another fib put about is that a famous gay pop star in the 80s who collapsed at a party. When his stomach was pumped the cause of his blackout was not drugs or alcohol but several pints of fresh spunk. Largely untrue, but it still went round my school like gospel.

Above: Feodor Rojankovski, Latvian (fl. 1920-1950)
Illustration from Pierre Louÿs' *Poésies Erotiques*
Opposite: Louis André Berthommé-Saint-André, French (1905–1977)
The Lazy Client

SAVOUR THE FLAVOUR

To spit or swallow? I recently read in a women's magazine a poll of young men's attitudes to this all-important question, one lad summed it up truthfully if perhaps not exactly like a gentleman – "if a girl doesn't swallow, it's only half a job." I reported this to my beloved who agreeably responded with "that's outrageous!" I smiled, nodded my agreement and patted him on the back. However, he was only part of the way through his pronouncement , "its

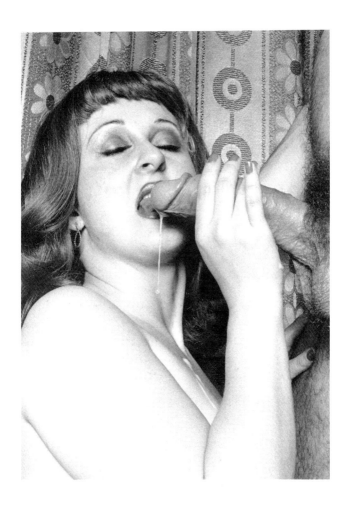

not *half* a job if the girl doesn't swallow, darling, it's *no job at all*'. Well, he's one of the lucky ones. Call me an old romantic but swilling a squirt of your man's essence if you're in love is just

---

Opposite: Eric Wilkins, British (contemporary)
Hunger V
Drinka Pinta Milk a Day
Above: Chinese School, Qing Dynasty (late 19th century)
Two Delicate Lotus Blossoms Mingle with the Jade Stalk
Scholars have pointed out that this may be an early exemplar of Oriental trampoline sex.

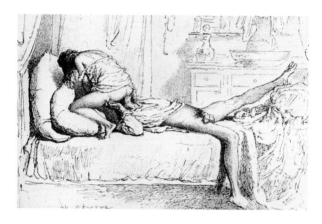

wonderful. Let's face it most people are very fond of their privates and have a close hands-on relationship with them. The very thought that someone else wants to kiss, caress and stroke those bits is very heaven, made all the more sweeter if they are, er, giving a little piece of themselves to you (one of the few times that the pious saying, 'it's better to give than to receive' is

Opposite: Jean Dulac, French (active 1920-1940)
Illustration from *Nous Deux*
She (thinks): 'I'm not sure I've got the best view.'
Above: Mihaly von Zichy, Hungarian (1827-1906)
Illustration from *Liebe*

not entirely true). There is such a thing, however, as being greedy. I have heard a story from a male friend who was told by a colleague that it was her fantasy to "drink a pint of cum". Her ambition was to milk every punter in her local and consume the results. My friend decided against making a donation to her *cock*tail, and declined the offer of a date. It's a sorry state, but there are still some double standards – you might want a cum-drinking slut in the bedroom, but don't necessarily want to see her sup at the crotches of the entire rugby club, or at least not all in one night.

The Erotic Review office has some strong opinions on ingestion. To the editor of the mighty organ, there is no question, it's simply ejaculatory etiquette to down it in one, girls. Unpalatable it may be, "like eating yeast mixed with raw sea urchin" she suggests, but making for

---

Opposite: Feodor Rojankovski, Latvian (fl. 1920-1950)
Illustration from *Paris Spring, 1933*
Cunninglingus – crafty application of tongue to female genitalia.
Following page: Anon, French (circa 1920)
Threesome (The DuPret Collection)
Somewhere between Paradise and Heaven.

the kitchen sink, with a bulging mouth and wide, panic-filled expression in order to hock it all up is downright rude. If one is prepared to chomp

---

Above: Mihaly von Zichy, Hungarian (1827-1906)
Illustration from *Liebe*
"Enough, you Devil! No! More, *more*, you Fiend!"
Opposite: Anon, French (circa 1900)
Tribadism I (The DuPret Collection)
"Ah, Cécile, you know so well how to please your Mistress!"

away in the time it takes to listen to an episode of *The Archers*, then swallowing at the grand finale isn't really much of a hardship, although I do think that *just* swallowing is proof enough of affection, there's no need to start showing off by gargling or blowing cum-bubbles, that's all a bit Thai prostitute if you ask me.

Such is the obsession with the volume of male ejaculate, that there have been two innocuous sounding references to it in rock music monikers. 10cc are supposed to have taken their name from the measurement of the average amount of seminal fluid produced on orgasm. And The Lovin' Spoonful is apparently the same. Funnily enough there used to

be a health food café in my home town with the same name. Come to think of it, their mushroom soup *did* have a familiar sour saltiness...

And what of the feminine ambrosia? The muff-lover encountering a nice clean pussy must contend (especially if they are good at it) with streams of female juices, which have their own particular flavour.

Opposite: Anon, French (circa 1900)
Leopard Skin (The DuPret Collection)
'Would you like to sin on a tiger skin with Elinor Glyn?
Or would you prefer to err with her on some other fur?'
Above: Léon Courbouleix, French (fl. 1930s)
Illustration from *Pour toi, pour moi*

Above: Anon, French (circa 1930)
The Tasting (The DuPret Collection)
"Come, Marie, let me taste you: are you salty and
briny? Or are you more like the forest's floor?"
Opposite: Louis André Berthommé-Saint-André, French (1905–1977)
Illustration from Alfred de Musset's *Gamiani*
A snug fit

The gastrobabble employed in description of the female *extrait* is worthy of Nigella Lawson's cookery column in the pages of *Vogue*. Journalist Victoria Moore wrote in *The Erotic Review* that the lush female folds has an "unctuous consistency… velvety texture and musky richness" in common with *pâté de fois gras*. And a couple of gems are to be found in *The Clitoral Truth* by Rebecca Chalker (Seven Stories Press):

Opposite: Anon, French (circa 1930)
Honeymoon Couple II (The DuPret Collection)
"Yes, we certainly *have* got damp."
Above: Cheripoulos, French (fl. 1920-1940)
Illustration to *La Roman de Violette*

Eric Wilkins, British (contemporary)
The Feast
"What a delicious... er, *spread*, Joanna."
Opposite: Franz, Marquis von Bayros, Austrian (1866-1924)
Divine Oral Decadence

Carol observes that her ejaculate tastes salty and briny, like buttered popcorn, or like the floor of the forest. Fanny says that hers hardly has any smell.

Gee girls, thanks. I can just see Jilly Goolden on the *Food and Drink* programme, gargling lust-juice like it's *Chateau Yquem* and pondering its woody tones and sharp gooseberry afterbite. And excuse me, but when was the last time you sampled the floor of forest? My boyfriend reckons he's had some twats that *looked* like it, as for the savour… he's unable to say.

Above: Chinese School, Qing Dynasty (late 19th century)
Parting the Petals of the Lotus Blossom
What more can we prosaic old Westerners add?
Opposite: Jean Dulac, French (active 1920-1940)
Illustration from *Nous Deux*
"When you said 'I want to pet your pussy',
I thought you meant Tiddles!"

Above: Louis André Berthommé-Saint-André, French (1905–1977)
Illustration from Paul Verlaine's *Œuvres Libres.*
"La, Sir! I see you practice those filthy French habits. Well, if I must endure it, I must, I suppose."
Opposite: Paul Avril, French (1849-1928)
Illustration from *De Figuris Veneris*

Carol is similarly loquacious on the subject of female ejaculation. She apparently ejaculated for years before she knew what was really happening and it makes her angry that she "had to struggle to understand something that's my birthright."

No need to get angry Carol dear, just get your head from up your own fundament and between a nice pair of thighs.

A more conventional comparison than Butterkist and woodland floors can be found in an email currently doing the rounds of bored office-workers. It is a dialogue between a couple on giving head, in response to her "I don't have to swallow," he inelegantly replies, "Swallowing a teaspoon full of cream is a hell of a lot easier than licking a dead fish." Well, he would say that, wouldn't he?

A more sensible voice on the subject of the crotch's finger-licking goodness is Dr David Delvin in his book *Sex Play* (Erotic Print Society), our good common-sense doctor says simply that women have different flavours, but is specific about something: "Redheads are usually the tangiest". I would love to read a general survey, if there is a man or woman out there with a large enough appetite and very strong tongue.

When it comes to pussy piquancy my friend
Oliver Maitland, puts it best. Maitland is the
author of *The Illustrated Book of Country Matters*
(Erotic Print Society) similar to this volume in
your hand but dedicated solely to the female sex

Above: Anon, French (circa 1930)
The Hesitant One (The DuPret Collection)
"Lower, Annette, lower!"
Opposite: Jean Dulac, French (active 1920-1940)
Illustration from *Nous Deux*
He (thinks): 'I wonder if this place is in the
Michelin guide? It rates at least two stars!'

organ, so you would expect him to be an excellent mouthpiece for cunt and its gourmet characteristics. In *Country Matters* he ruminates upon epicurean delights ranging from pheromone-heavy truffles to the Voigner grape to "a light, quite lemony Hollandaise sauce," but even the bon vivant himself finally resorts to:

> In the end a fanny tastes like a fanny. They all taste different and each tastes different on different occasions.

I am fortunate enough to be intimately acquainted with someone whose favourite tipple is fanny-batter. My love tells me that I am "effervescent" and that I "taste of the sea". I hope he isn't euphemistically saying 'like an Alka Seltzer dropped in the coast off Blackpool.' My sweetheart is also extremely fond of oysters. Apart from their zinc content, taste and texture, the aphrodisiac propensities of an oyster owes

Anon, French (circa 1900)
Tribadism II (The DuPret Collection)
"And you say this is the sort of thing that will get us the vote, Emily?"

something to its resemblance to a slippery cunt.
Before our courtship he launched into a
monologue extolling the virtues of the shellfish. It
was pure audio erotica, how he liked the feel of
luscious, viscous mass in his mouth and insisted it
was vital to drink the water from the shell
afterwards. I interpreted the whole speech as
flirtation and heavily scented with cunnilingual

Above: Anon, French (circa 1900)
Tribadism III (The DuPret Collection)
"My husband must never know."
"No, Madame. Of course not!"
Opposite: Louis André Berthommé-Saint-André, French
(1905–1977)
Illustration from Alfred de Musset's *Gamiani*
'Oh *rapture!*"

code. I was brought back to earth when he finished by saying, "Of course, you're not supposed to, but *I* like to chew them once or twice before swallowing". I found I had my legs tightly crossed.

'Funky' (i.e. rotten-tasting) spunk can supposedly be controlled by regulation of what the man eats. If this is so (sexperts are divided on this one) then it's common sense rules – curries/chilli

Anon, German School (circa 1920)
The Garden of Eden
Well, it had to all start *somewhere*…

produce a spicy aftertaste, for a sweeter effect try sugary foods or cinnamon and, it's true, asparagus *does* result in acquired sour base notes. And, weight watchers, calories *shmalories* ok? It's no more fattening than a rice cake, so that's one myth out of the window. There is no known method of controlling the feminine pungency from within, but as long as you're healthy, then cleanliness is the only golden rule. No-one's going to get much lip-action if they are offering up rancid genitalia, now are they?

BON APPETIT

The practise of oral sex is not only about the top joining the tail, it's a full physical and psychological experience. A frequent comment on giving oral sex is that a pleasure for the fellatrice/cunnilinguist is what happens bodily all over.

Between lovers the sensations of giving and receiving are exquisite.

A love letter I recently found was a paean to oral gratification:

Gaston Barret, French (fl. 1950s)
Illustration to *Lettres à la Marquise, l'Adam lascif*
"This is somehow all so… *organic*, Miss Beaufort."

I love to pour drinks down your neck and see your lips and tongue taste the fizz and the alcohol and melt. I love to feed you watching you swallow and smile. And I love it when you take me in your soft lips and your delicious tongue and makes me want to come. I love you dancing on my tongue, I feel your whole body is balanced in my mouth: streams of civet and musk cascading down my throat over my lips soaking the bed. Your thighs bruising my cheeks, your oil and scent is sweet… I want to suck you where you are wet, so deeply that you twist above me and my tongue tastes you inside, so deep inside, pulling you onto me and eating you up until there is nothing left but a transparent shred of knicker.

(I don't know who it was from, in fact I can't be certain that it was actually intended for me, but surely I'd *remember* a boy like that if I met him?)

Many men find the act of cunnilingus almost as physically exciting for themselves as the recipient female. Nancy Friday's collections of

Opposite: **Louis André Berthommé-Saint-André, French (1905–1977)**
Illustration from Paul Verlaine's *Œuvres Libres.*
"Lick harder, you lascivious young Lascar!"
Above: **Anon, French (circa 1900)**
Tribadism IV **(The DuPret Collection)**
"Oh, *Madame!*"

sexual fantasies feature a great deal of women reaching climax through daydreaming about only giving head. In *Men in Love* (Arrow books) she remarks upon how often men include giving oral sex in their fantasies. Having written to her to assist her research, many of them were falling over themselves to point out how much is in it for them. 'Donald' is a fan,

> I love to look at a cunt up close; to smell the warm, faintly musky odour... to feel the soft smooth walls of the cunt with my tongue – especially when the cunt's moisture is providing the lubricant for my tongue; to savour the faint sweet taste as I lap, and even the sound is a turn-on...

'Fred' prefers to:

Opposite: Anon, French (circa 1910)
The Armchair (The DuPret Collection)
"Are you beginning to see the advantages of equal rights for women now?"
Following page: Léon Courbouleix, French (fl. 1930s)
Suzon en Vacances
By far the most pleasant wake up call.

...examine it with childlike adoration, noting in great detail the very minute anatomical differences in each sweet pussy...

and 'Russell' says,

I love the fragrance of a woman's genitals, the softness of the vulva, the slightly sweet, salty taste of her vaginal secretions.

I would like to leave you in an ideal world, one where you and your lover have a mutual understanding of oral sex and similar appetites for it. The most passionate way to worship and be worshipped is the *soixante-neuf* or, as I have seen it referred to, 'the breakfast of champions'. Suddenly I'm all hungry again... bon appetit